Sid the

Written by Abigail Steel

Illustrated by Diane Ewen

Sid the kid can tip the pan.

Sid the kid got the mat.

Sid the kid got the cap.

Sid the kid got in a gap!

Kim got Sid the kid!

Talk about the story

Ask your child these questions:

1 What kind of animal was Sid?

2 How did Sid escape?

3 What was the farmer's name in the story?

4 What do you think was the naughtiest thing Sid did?

5 What farm animals can you name?

6 What's your favourite farm animal? Why?

Can your child retell the story using their own words?